Little Acts of

Self-care

COUNTLESS WAYS TO
RELAX MIND, BODY & SPIRIT

This edition published in 2019
By SJG Publishing, HP22 6NF, UK

Author: Rebecca Dickinson
Cover design: Milestone Creative
Contents design: seagulls.net

ISBN: 978-1-911517-73-3

Printed in China

10 9 8 7 6 5 4 3 2 1

'To love oneself is the beginning of a lifelong romance.'

Oscar Wilde

Introduction

When was the last time you made an
appointment with yourself? Or marked
out a section in your diary to do
something you wanted to do, rather than
something you were required to do?
Many of us lead such on-the-go lives that
we push our own needs and desires to
one side, for the benefit of everyone else.

This can be ok for a while, but sooner or later cracks will appear. And, left untended, those cracks can become deep cavities that seep into your physical and mental health, eating away at your happiness and potential.

Self-care really is as simple as it sounds: it's about listening to, and meeting, the needs of your body, mind and spirit. But while it sounds ridiculously obvious, self-care can be surprisingly difficult to put into practice.

There is a worrying misconception that self-care is selfish. It's not! However strong, selfless or stoical you are, if you don't take care of yourself you won't be able to take care of anyone else. And you won't be at your best when it comes to work, home and relationships. Ultimately, you'll end up burnt out and exhausted.

This book explains why self-care is so important and how to make it part of your lifestyle. It will help to dispel the negative thoughts that create a roadblock to well-being, by reassuring you that you are never too busy, or too unworthy, to make self-care a priority.

You'll discover all sorts of ways to be kind to yourself, from the momentary to the life-changing, the once-a-day to the one-off, whatever your budget or situation. So stop feeling guilty and start looking after yourself – and yes, that includes doing things you enjoy! Because self-care matters as much as you do.

The Foundations of Self-Care

Shhh!

Self-care starts with acknowledging the way we speak to ourselves, and learning to silence our inner critic. You know – the one that tells you you're too selfish or shy, or whispers that you're not sassy or attractive, or clever or witty enough. Don't listen!

Many of us are all too quick to judge ourselves and put ourselves down. We tell ourselves we're not up to the job, we don't look right, we don't fit in, we're not capable. But what if a friend said that about themselves? The chances are you would contradict them, help them to see their strengths, rather than their weaknesses. What would you tell them? Now try saying the same to yourself. From now on, every time that inner critic appears and you start to doubt yourself, talk to yourself as if you were speaking to a friend, with the same voice of encouragement and reassurance.

'Do not speak badly of yourself. For the warrior within hears your words and is lessened by them.'

David Gemmell

ACCEPT THE CARE OF OTHERS

When you don't feel worthy of self-care, it can be hard to accept acts of care from other people, too. To welcome kindness into your life, you need to believe in your own self-worth. Only then can you fully accept that others want to be good to you. So tell yourself you deserve to be happy, and remember: it's ok to receive as well as give. In fact it's more than ok, it's essential. We all need to be supported ourselves, in order to be able to support others.

Close your eyes and remember a time when you were blown away by something someone did for you. It could have been someone close to you, or a complete stranger. How did it make you feel? Write it down if you like, so you can come back to it whenever you need to.

'Change your thoughts and you change your world.'
Norman Vincent Peale

LITTLE ACTS OF SELF-CARE

The fact that you're reading this book means you're already thinking about self-care, which is a brilliant start. Think of the following acts as the fuel you need to live your best possible life.

- Love yourself unconditionally, as a parent loves a child.

- Set aside time for yourself every day, even if it's just a few minutes.

- Accept all the imperfections and limitations that make you human.

- Cherish all the quirks that make you unique.

- Do at least one thing you love every day, however tiny or trivial.

- Refrain from comparing yourself to others.

- Reward yourself.

- Forgive yourself.

Micro-Acts
OF SELF-CARE

Self-care isn't all about shopping sprees and spa days (although we probably wouldn't say no to either of those!) More often, it's about sprinkling a little confetti over daily life.

- Have a slice of lemon with your glass of water.

- Moisturize.

- Stop to smell the roses – literally. Or the next flower you encounter.

- Take off or undo your bra (or tie, or belt) in the evening, or when you get home from work.

- Wash your bedding – or just the pillowcase, if you don't have time for the whole lot.

- Sit down for meals rather than wolfing a sandwich on the run, or eating while multi-tasking.

- Buy the posh soap, the expensive chocolate, or your favorite cheese, once in a while.

'None of us are getting out of here alive, so please stop treating yourself like an afterthought. Eat the delicious food. Walk in the sunshine. Jump in the ocean. Say the truth that you're carrying in your heart like hidden treasure. Be silly. Be kind. Be weird. There's no time for anything else.'

Anthony Hopkins

'Be kind to yourself so you can be happy enough to be kind to the world.'

Misha Collins

Love the Skin You're In

AND EVERYTHING THAT COMES WITH IT

To practise self-care, you need to be happy with your own DNA. That's because internalising your own value is crucial to believing you are worthy of self-care. Of course, we all have things we'd like to change about ourselves, but this isn't the place for that.

What's more, once you begin to acknowledge your own self-worth and start treating yourself with love and kindness, you'll be in a better position to treat other people the same way. So start making a difference to yourself today.

BE YOUR OWN

Hero

Use the following prompts to help you think about your own special qualities. If you get stuck, ask someone who knows you for suggestions.

- Think of five things you're good at. Whether it's standing on your head, telling jokes or creating amazing cakes, we all have talents.

- Say out loud five things you like about the way you look. No, your little toe doesn't count!

- List five things you've achieved in your life. It could be anything from keeping a pot plant alive to running a marathon.

- Write down the names of five people (or animals) who care about you or depend upon you. Include pets if you want to, but make sure to mention some humans, too.

- Think of five compliments you've received. This can be tricky, but try to think of occasions when someone has congratulated you on a piece of work for example, or remarked on a new haircut or even a great photograph you took.

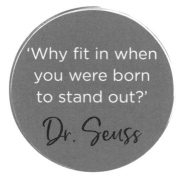

'Why fit in when you were born to stand out?'

Dr. Seuss

LITTLE ACTS OF SELF-CARE TO CUT YOURSELF SOME SLACK

The world can be demanding enough without trying to be a superhero. Sometimes self-care is just about making life that little bit easier.

- Do your grocery shopping online and get it delivered to your house.

- Skimp on the household chores – a bit of dirt is good for the immune system anyway!

- Give up, or drastically reduce, the amount of ironing you do. Think how much time you could save by ditching the ironing board.

- Save water - don't wash clothes unless they really need it!

- Cook once, eat twice – cook in bulk and freeze portions for when you're short of time or energy.

- Get a cleaner if you can afford to, even if it's just occasionally.

Hug More!

A hug is the language of compassion.

And guess what? Scientists have proved that hugging increases levels of the 'love hormone' oxytocin, which is beneficial for both physical and emotional health. Regular, genuine hugs can help lower our stress levels, reduce depression and fatigue, improve blood pressure, heart health and even build immunity. In short, hugs don't just feel good, they do good, too.

According to research, a hug needs to last for 20 seconds to be effective – so don't let go too soon!

Better still, hugging is just as beneficial for the person being hugged as the one doing the hugging, so everyone's a winner. What's more, hugs are completely free. So get cuddling!

Piglet: 'How do you spell love?'

Pooh: 'You don't spell it, you feel it.'

AA Milne

Smile!

As the saying goes, 'smile and the world smiles with you.' Never underestimate the power of a smile. Although it might feel strange at first, try smiling at people you pass on the street, sit next to on the bus, or stand next to in a line. Once you get used to it you'll discover how good it makes you feel, especially when you get a smile in return.

You might even end up striking up conversation. Give it a go for yourself!

'A warm smile is the universal language of kindness.'

William Arthur Ward

TAKE TIME OUT

Many of us live such frantic lives that taking time out is one of the most powerful ways in which we can express self-care. See how many of these you can manage:

- Put your phone away and give the person in front of you 100% of your attention. Even better, turn it off!

- Forget the chores and set aside a whole evening or weekend to spend with your partner, family, or friends.

- Meet someone for a coffee without setting a time by which you need to rush off.

- Make the effort to travel to see a friend or relative who lives far away.

- Take your full lunch break and get out of the office, even if others don't.

- Visit someone you miss and do nothing but chat.

'Strive not to be a success but rather to be of value.'

Albert Einstein

LITTLE ACTS OF SELF-CARE TO
Warm the Heart

- Buy yourself a small succulent or other houseplant and notice how good it feels to nurture something.

- Plant a rose bush and experience the delight of watching it bloom. Choose one that's strongly scented and drink in the fragrance.

- Make bread from scratch, then eat it fresh from the oven.

- Treat yourself to a magazine rather than just reading articles online.

- Relax in a candlelit bath.

- Think of a time when you were really happy, or did something amazing, then allow yourself to relive the experience in your head.

'The best and most beautiful things in the world cannot be seen or even touched. They must be felt with the heart.'

Helen Keller

LITTLE ACTS OF SELF-CARE FOR

The Body

When we exercise self-care over our physical selves, we also feel better emotionally and psychologically. The mind doesn't live in splendid isolation from the rest of the body, or vice versa. So when we take care of our health, we also boost our self-esteem, which in turn helps us to face the world with gusto.

On the other hand, our thoughts, feelings, beliefs, and attitudes can positively or negatively affect our physical health. One simple example of this is that during periods of stress the immune system is weakened, which is why you're more likely to come down with a cold when you're going through a rough time.

Just as a runner prepares for a race by having a training schedule, we too can stay in shape for the marathon of life by making little acts of self-care part of our routine.

'Our bodies are our gardens, to the which our wills are gardeners.'

William
Shakespeare

EAT BEAUTIFUL

Food

Eating well is at the very heart of self-care. It's also one of the easiest acts of self-care to put into practice. After all, we all need to eat, so you might as well make sure that what you put into your mouth does you good as well as tasting good.

The good news is that eating beautifully doesn't mean spending a fortune on the exotic, expensive, unpronounceable products commonly found on Instagram: the so-called superfoods.

The key to eating for self-care is to include a wide range of fresh, nutritious and energizing foods, and to avoid processed foods as much as possible, while indulging in the original superfoods: ordinary fruits and vegetables!

'Let food be thy medicine and medicine be thy food.'

Hippocrates

LITTLE ACTS OF SELF-CARE
FOR EATING
Beautifully

- **Eat more plants** – if you make one change to your diet, do this! Upping your intake of fruit and veg is a guaranteed way to get more vitamins, minerals and antioxidants into your body. You could kick-off by having 'meat-free Mondays.' No meat on your plate means more room for veg.

- **Eat real food** – if it sounds like it was grown in a laboratory it's probably not worth eating.

- **Buy organic when possible** – organic foods aren't just lower in chemicals and pesticides, they are also higher in vitamins and minerals.

According to recent research, eating organic fruit and veg is equivalent to getting an extra 1–2 portions a day. If you struggle with the cost, try shopping at the end of the day when there are likely to be price reductions.

- **Don't beat yourself up** – if going organic isn't an option, remember it's far better to eat non-organic fruit and veg than it is to eat none at all, or to rely on convenience food.

- **Grow your own** – growing a little, or a lot, of your own food is a delicious and rewarding act of self-care, and a cheap way of eating organically. What's more, it really isn't difficult. Don't have a garden? Many crops like herbs and salad leaves grow brilliantly in containers. So grab a pot, some soil and some seeds, and simply follow the instructions on the packet. As well as the health benefits, you'll have the added satisfaction of watching your food's journey from seed to plate.

- **Go easy on the sugar** – as well as increasing the risk of diabetes and other conditions, sugar provides a short-lived high followed by a mood-zapping energy slump.

- **Ditch the diet** – healthy eating should equal happy eating, so concentrate on healthy foods that you enjoy and make them part of your lifestyle, rather than focusing on avoidance and restriction.

- **Eat a little of what you fancy** – yes, you can have your cake and eat it. Cutting down on sugar doesn't mean avoiding it entirely. We all need a treat now and then and allowing yourself the things you like is an important act of self-care.

'Real food doesn't have ingredients. Real food is ingredients.'

Jamie Oliver

LITTLE ACTS OF SELF-CARE

FOR WHEN YOU NEED A

Boost

There's no doubt that a balanced, healthy diet is better than vitamin supplements. However, there are times when we all need a little pick-me-up, especially during or after periods of illness or stress. Whether you are feeling run down, or just run off your feet, here are a few useful supplements.

- **Magnesium** – essential for muscles and nerves, magnesium is found in leafy green vegetables, nuts, seeds, beans and whole grains. However, many of us, especially women and the elderly, don't get enough which can cause fatigue, muscle weakness and cramps, among other symptoms. You could take magnesium as a supplement or sprinkle some magnesium flakes into your bath, as it can be absorbed through the skin.

- **Vitamin D** – the so-called sunshine vitamin is vital for healthy bones, teeth, muscles and the immune system. Small amounts are found in egg yolks, oily fish and dairy products but the vast majority is produced in the skin on exposure to UVB sunlight. Depending on where you live, a supplement may be essential at certain times of the year.

- **Omega 3** – this is another essential nutrient which is often lacking from modern diets. As well as protecting against cardiovascular disease, Omega-3 fatty acids are vital for healthy cells, joints and brain function. Good food sources include oily fish, nuts and seeds, but if you don't eat these regularly, a supplement could be a good investment.

- **Vitamin B12** – this vital vitamin is found in foods of animal origin such as meat, fish, eggs and dairy. Although some B12 also occurs in yeast extract, it's hard to get enough if you follow a vegan diet, so supplements are recommended. Low levels of vitamin B12, and other B vitamins, may be linked to depression.

- **Iron** – women in particular often lack iron, resulting in tiredness and dizziness. Red meat provides the best source of iron, but it's also available in leafy vegetables like kale and spinach, as well as pulses, eggs and nuts. Iron is more easily absorbed if eaten with vitamin C, so try drinking a glass of orange juice with your eggs or steak and ask for a blood test if you think you may be deficient.

LITTLE ACTS OF SELF-CARE
FOR NON-GUILTY
Pleasure

Who said healthy eating was gruelling? Here are some little ways to treat your taste buds and your body at the same time.

- **Dark chocolate** – it's official: good quality chocolate is a great source of antioxidants which help protect against disease-causing free radicals. What's more, dark chocolate is rich in other good stuff too, such as flavanols which can help keep your heart and cholesterol levels healthy. So tuck in!

- **Avocado** – no longer to be shunned for the calorie content, avocados are finally having a moment and with good reason. They are one of the healthiest foods you can eat, packed with lashings of vitamins, minerals, antioxidants and vital healthy fats.

- Peanut butter (or other nut butter) – high in protein and much more nutritious on toast than a dollop of jam.

- Butter – yes, butter! Real butter, preferably from grass-fed cows, is a much healthier choice than low-fat spreads which are full of harmful trans fats. In fact, research has shown that margarine actually increases the risk of heart disease, unlike butter. Butter from grass-fed cows is full of healthy substances, such as butyric acid, which has anti-inflammatory properties.

- Smoothies – although not a substitute for eating whole fruit and veg, smoothies are a good way to get loads of nutrients in one go, especially when you're in a hurry. The healthiest smoothies contain veg as well as fruit. So why not invest in a blender and start whizzing up your own?

Drink Up

No, not that kind of drink! Though there's nothing wrong with a cold beer or glass of wine in moderation, as long as you're drinking loads of the clear stuff too.

Our bodies are made up of around 60 percent water and our brains a sloshing 74 percent! So upping your H_2O intake is a no-brainer.

Scientists have shown that being as little as two percent dehydrated can reduce your ability to concentrate and function, even when you don't feel thirsty.

It's recommended that women consume around 8 cups of water a day, and men 10 cups, with around 70—80 percent of that coming from drinks.

LITTLE ACTS OF SELF-CARE TO HELP YOU STAY HYDRATED

- Carry a water bottle wherever you go, whatever the weather.

- Swap one of your daily teas or coffees for a herbal tea instead.

- Try hot water with lemon. Bonus points if you can make this your morning wake-up drink.

- Eat foods with a high water content such as watermelon, celery, cucumber, tomatoes and grapefruit.

- Cut back on caffeine and alcohol which are both dehydrating, especially in large quantities.

'Water is life's matter and matrix, mother and medium. There is no life without water.'

Albert Szent Gyorgyi

Go to Bed!

Nothing helps us to get up and face the day quite like a good night's sleep. Sleep is fundamental to our health and happiness, as anyone who's prone to insomnia will appreciate. Quite simply, a decent night's sleep makes us feel human. Not to mention more pleasant to be around!

Physically, sleep gives the body a chance to regenerate itself as, during sleep, hormones are released that stimulate muscle growth and repair. If we don't sleep enough, the body doesn't have time for this to happen. Being sleep-deprived messes with our memory, slows our reaction times and gives us that horrible 'brain-fog.' A regular lack of sleep can also increase the risk of conditions like heart disease and diabetes, as well as mood disorders like depression and anxiety.

The amount of sleep we need varies between individuals, but most of us need between seven and nine hours a night. When we get less than six hours, we lose some of the REM (rapid eye movement) phase of sleep, making it harder to absorb new information and making the simplest of tasks a struggle. So do yourself a favour and get more sleep!

'By helping us keep the world in perspective, sleep gives us a chance to refocus on the essence of who we are. And in that place of connection, it is easier for the fears and concerns of the world to drop away.'

Arianna Huffington,
The Sleep Revolution

LITTLE ACTS OF SELF-CARE FOR A

Better Night's Sleep

'And the night shall be filled with music,
And the cares, that infest the day,
Shall fold their tents like the Arabs,
and silently steal away.'

Henry Wadsworth Longfellow

- Limit or avoid caffeine after 2pm.

- Adopt a 'bedtime routine' – a series of wind-down activities you do every night to tell yourself it's time for bed.

- Keep your bedroom cool and dark.

- Turn off devices in the evenings as the light emitted by screens stimulates the brain.

- Don't check the time through the night.

- Build activity into your day – people who exercise regularly tend to sleep better. Exercise also helps us to manage stress, a common cause of sleepless nights.

- Try a soothing drink like chamomile or warm milk before bed.

- Eat turkey – it's a great source of tryptophan, an amino acid that helps boost the sleep-inducing hormone melatonin. Other sources include: chicken, milk and dairy, bananas, nuts and seeds.

LITTLE ACTS OF SELF-CARE

LITTLE ACTS OF SELF-CARE
THAT ARE ALMOST EFFORTLESS

- Paint your nails – or just file and polish.

- Treat yourself to some nice hand cream.

- Have a massage – if you can't afford a professional one ask a friend, partner, or even children, if you have them.

- Make your own face mask by mashing up an avocado and mixing it with one tablespoon of honey. Delicious!

- Go to bed an hour earlier.

- Strrreeeetch – reach up high from side to side and swing your arms. And repeat. Stretching gets the oxygen flowing and loosens everything up.

Move it!

Along with eating well and getting enough sleep, the third ingredient for optimum health and happiness is exercise. Before you groan at the thought of stepping on a treadmill or signing up for boot camp, there are plenty of other ways to get your heart pumping a bit faster than normal – from gardening to salsa, dog-walking to scooting.

As well as keeping us physically fit, exercise is a great way to get the endorphins flowing, for that 'feel-good' sensation. What's more, being fit lowers the risk of serious illnesses like heart disease and type 2 diabetes.

The most important thing is to find an activity that you enjoy and can do regularly. Ideally, don't limit yourself to one type of exercise, but add some variety so you work different muscle groups.

LITTLE ACTS OF SELF-CARE

To Get You Moving

There's no need to splash out on a pricey gym membership – exercise can be anything that works your muscles. Yes, that does include household chores, but that's hardly an act of self-care, so try some of the following instead.

- Grab a lunchtime swim. If you've got small children, go for a moonlight dip when they're in bed.

- Use your local park – run, walk, throw a frisbee, kick a ball; research shows there are added benefits to exercising outdoors. Some parks also have free outdoor gyms.

- Follow along with free exercise videos on YouTube.

- Get on your bike – a weekend cycle is a great way to unwind and improve fitness at the same time.

- Dance around the kitchen to your favorite tunes.

- Get off the couch – if you enjoy watching TV to relax, why not try a few squats or crunches during the ad breaks?

- Use the stairs not the lift – yes, you've heard it before, but every step really does count.

- Sex – just in case you needed another excuse.

LITTLE ACTS OF SELF-CARE FOR
Protecting Your Back

It seems odd that we use the phrase 'pain in the proverbial,' when more us of would relate to 'pain in the back'.

Back pain is incredibly common; up to 80 percent of people develop back problems at some point during their lives, and it can have a massive impact on everyday life. So spinal self-care is something we all need to be aware of – preferably before it becomes a 'pain in the back.'

One of the most important ways to care your back is to keep moving and to avoid sitting down for long periods of time without a break. Humans weren't designed for chairs so if you need to spend a lot of time on one, make sure you keep getting up and down.

Some types of back pain are caused by specific conditions and may need medical help*, but the majority are down to lifestyle, which is why self-care is so important. Look after your body and your body will look after you.

* If your back pain is very severe, or you have other symptoms too, then see a doctor.

'Take care of your body. It's the only place you have to live.'

Jim Rohn

LITTLE ACTS OF SELF-CARE TO

Save Your Back

- **Play musical chairs** – if you have a job that requires bums on seats, make sure you get up from your desk every 30 minutes. Have a stretch, a walk, a wriggle – ignore any funny looks. Even if you don't have back problems, do it to help prevent them in the future.

- **Correct your posture at work** – slumping over a desk all day shortens your hip flexors and puts stress on the lower back. Keep your feet flat on the floor, with knees just below hip level. Alternatively, instead of sitting on a chair, try a stability ball which engages the core muscles, or even a kneeling chair or standup desk.

- Work that core – the deep torso muscles, or 'core', play an important role in keeping your back strong and supported, as well as helping with posture. Look up exercises on YouTube or join a Pilates class.

- Lift carefully – bend your knees, not your back, and avoid twisting when lifting. And use common sense!

- Walk it, baby – along with all the other benefits, walking increases blood flow to the spine which helps with healing.

MORE ACTS OF SELF-CARE TOWARD A HEALTHIER LIFE-STYLE

- Swap plastic food boxes and drink bottles for glass or stainless steel, or containers that are BPA-free. This simple change prevents the chemicals in plastics from getting into food.

- Change non-stick pans to ones that don't contain BPA.

- Keep your bowels moving daily – we all poop, and pooping regularly helps keep your gut healthy and removes toxins. Eat more fibre if necessary.

- Check the ingredients in shampoos, body lotions and other cosmetics and choose products that are free from chemicals like parabens and phthalates, as these can have negative health impacts.

- Avoid processed food as much as possible. If you don't have time to cook, a baked potato with beans is still better than a microwave-meal.

LITTLE ACTS OF
SELF-CARE FOR

The Mind

Are you always on a mission? Do you feel
constantly wired, like you're stuck inside the
spin cycle of a washing machine? The busier
you are, the more important it is to make
time to relax. Because when you're constantly
strung out, always on the go, striving for the
next big thing, the only way out is burnout.

In today's non-stop world, calm can be an elusive ingredient. Yet relaxation is integral to our happiness and wellbeing and we all need to switch off and log out on a regular basis. Taking time out allows us to live in the moment and to find peace within our surroundings and ourselves.

Relaxation is also critical for our health; when we live in a prolonged state of stress this causes our bodies to churn out extra cortisol, the stress hormone that can disrupt hormonal balance and increase the likelihood of illness.

So make it your mission to include a bit of relaxation in your day and pledge to take some downtime. Even a small amount will make your life so much happier and more fulfilling, and that, after all, is the only thing worth striving for.

'Life is not measured by the number of breaths we take, but by the moments that take our breath away.'

Maya Angelou

FOCUS ON
YOUR BREATH

Learning to breathe more deeply helps you to feel more calm and can counteract anxiety. Try to practice this technique every day. Loosen any tight clothing, then sit, stand or lie down, just as long as you feel comfortable.

Breathe in through your nose, letting your breath fill your body.

As you breathe in, count to four.

Keep your shoulders down and relaxed, and place your hand on your stomach, noticing it rise as you breathe in and fall as you breathe out.

Without pausing or holding your breath, breathe out through your mouth, counting to five.

Try to do this for three to five minutes.

FOCUS ON YOUR

Feelings

Just because your feelings aren't logical, doesn't mean they're not valid. If something feels real to you, then it's real. And just because someone else is in a worse situation than you are, it doesn't mean you're not allowed to feel sad, too. There will always be someone worse off, but that doesn't mean you need to feel guilty.

So stop trying to dismiss your emotions; you can't just waft them away. Acknowledging your feelings is an important part of self-care and finding inner peace.

"Do you ever have days when everything feels... Not Very Okay At All?"

Piglet nodded his head sagely. "Oh yes,"said Piglet. "I definitely have those days."

AA Milne

And... Relax

It doesn't matter how busy you are, you need to carve out time to relax. You might not be able to go on a yoga retreat, or even join a weekly class, but there are plenty of other ways to give your mind a break. Often, it's the tiny, regular acts of relaxation that make the biggest difference.

And when we take time out to recharge, we return to whatever it was we were doing before with renewed vigour. If you can't take time to relax, you need to make time.

'A field that has rested gives a beautiful crop.'

Ovid

FROM ONE TO TEN: LITTLE ACTS OF SELF-CARE FOR WHEN YOU ONLY HAVE A FEW MINUTES TO SPARE

- **One minute:** give yourself a head massage.

- **Two minutes:** sit on a park bench.

- **Three minutes:** dance.

- **Four minutes:** listen to your favorite song.

- **Five minutes:** read a magazine article.

- **Six minutes:** sing.

- **Seven minutes:** watch the clouds.

- **Eight minutes:** color in a mandala – you don't have to finish it; come back to it every day.

- **Nine minutes:** do a spot of gardening. Plant chile seeds, sow salad in a container.

- **Ten minutes:** sit down to eat – it's better for your digestion, too.

'Don't walk
behind me,
I may not lead.
Don't walk in
front of me,
I may not follow.
Just walk beside
me and be
my friend.'

Albert Camus

SELF-CARE AND

Mental Health

Every year, one in four of us will experience a mental health problem. Depression and anxiety are both wretchedly common and, according to the World Health Organization, depression is the leading cause of ill health and disability in the world today, affecting more than 300 million people globally.

The symptoms of mental illnesses may be invisible, but the effects can be debilitating, impacting on relationships and friendships, and even the ability to do everyday tasks.

If you're struggling with your mental health, the first act of self-care is to accept that your condition is real. The second is to accept that it's not your fault, in the same way as catching flu is not your fault. And the third is to get the support you need.

Self-care is not a panacea for mental illness; medication and other treatments are often necessary too. However, self-care helps to counter the negative thoughts that tell us we are not worthy, affirming our value at a time when we need it most.

'We must try not to sink beneath our anguish [...] but battle on.'

JK Rowling

LITTLE ACTS OF SELF-CARE FOR WHEN YOU'RE FEELING ANXIOUS OR DEPRESSED

• **Let people know** – you may feel withdrawn and like you want to shut friends and family out, but try to be honest and let them know it's not you, it's the illness. People can see a broken arm but they may not be able to see depression or anxiety.

• **Accept practical support** – if you're struggling to keep on top of things, allow others do small chores like putting out the garbage, doing some washing, shopping, or cooking a meal.

• **Tell yourself it's ok not to be ok** – you don't need to put on a brave face; being honest about the way you feel is an important act of self-care and also helps to break down the stigma surrounding mental illness.

• **Do things you enjoy even when you don't feel like it** – when it's a struggle just to get out of bed, even the tiniest act of self-care can have a positive effect. Try going for a walk in the countryside, or even round the block, doing some craft, or watching a film.

- **Get some sleep** – poor sleep can be an unwelcome symptom of mental illness. Try lavender oil or camomile tea, or even placing some worry dolls under your pillow at night. Even if they don't work, just verbalizing your anxieties can be a useful exercise.

- **Seek support** – whether it's therapy, joining a support group or even reading self-help books, don't try to ride the storm alone.

- **Write it down** – writing is great therapy and keeping track of your thoughts and emotions in a journal can help you to make sense of them.

- **Get help** – if your low days are overwhelming or you have any thoughts of harming yourself then seek help immediately.

Forgive Yourself

Nobody's perfect and that includes you! So the next time you spill your coffee, turn up late, lose your temper or an important document, burn the dinner or drop the toast (buttered side down), be gentle with yourself. Speak to yourself with the voice of self-care rather than self-criticism. We all make mistakes, just make amends when possible, and move on.

'Do as the heavens have done, forget your evil; With them forgive yourself.'

William Shakespeare

LEARN TO SAY 'NO'

Are you the kind of person who blurts out 'yes' whenever anyone asks for your time? While kindness is a virtue, it's important to make sure that saying 'yes' to everyone else doesn't mean saying 'no' to self-care.

Perhaps you're the kind of person who likes to please, or feels compelled to say 'yes' so that people will like you. The problem with this is that you can end up being taken for granted; you become over-stretched, over-scheduled and stressed out under the weight of other people's requests.

There are times when saying 'no' is not so much an act of self-care as an act of self-preservation. If you find it hard to turn people down, try telling them you need to check your diary and will let them know tomorrow.

If you still can't bring yourself to say 'no', then tell a little white lie: say you have an appointment, a bad back, family commitments, whatever works, and put it down to an act of self-care.

'Women, in particular, need to keep an eye on their physical and mental health, because if we're scurrying to and from appointments and errands, we don't have a lot of time to take care of ourselves. We need to do a better job of putting ourselves higher on our own 'to do' list.'

Michelle Obama

HAVE A DIGITAL DETOX

Believe it or not, there are more mobile devices on the planet than there are humans. This staggering fact means that we are now simultaneously more connected and disconnected than ever. We can communicate with people on the other side of the world as if they were next door, yet often we don't know the names of the people who live 60 feet away.

What's more, many of us find it difficult to leave our cell phones alone for more than three minutes. Whether it's checking emails, using apps, or lurking on Facebook, we are constantly online. But the irony of social media is that it's often anything but social.

Electronic media provides a wealth of opportunities and conveniences – we can order a taxi, study, shop, or check our bank balances with our thumbs. Yet there is also the danger that we become persistent absentees from the real world.

LITTLE ACTS OF SELF-CARE FOR A

- Turn off notifications – doing this means your phone won't ping every time you get a new like or comment. And resist the temptation to check every few minutes!

- Unfollow accounts of people who consistently make you feel inferior by posting about their wonderful lives and achievements.

- Refrain from posting only the edited highlights of your own life. Keep it real with the good, the bad and the ugly.

- Unsubscribe from email lists – special offers, websites you never visit, blogs you don't read, influencers you don't want to be influenced by; just get rid of them. They only clog up your inbox and your time.

- Make the dinner table a tech-free zone – put all devices away before eating and chat to the people you live with instead.

- Make Sundays screen-free – have a completely screenless day and revel in the freedom.

'The difference between technology and slavery is that slaves are fully aware that they are not free.'

Nassim Nicholas Taleb

GET WITH THE FLOW

Have you ever been so absorbed in an activity that it's as if time stopped and the world around you melted away?

In positive psychology, this is called being in a 'state of flow'. It happens when we become so immersed in whatever we are doing that we forget everything else around us. Athletes call this entering 'the zone'.

For a state of flow to happen, we need to stretch our skills so that the activity is challenging but not impossible. Being in the zone boosts concentration, performance and self-esteem. What's more, it leaves no space for worrying about the other stuff: the laundry, the cooking, the deadlines, the Monday mornings.

We all need a passion, so discover yours and make it a life-enhancing act of self-care.

'Everything vanishes around me, and works are born as if out of the void.'

Paul Klee

Little Acts
OF SELF-CARE
FOR ZONING OUT

Is there something you've always wanted to try? An activity you once loved but no longer have time for? Well, put yourself first for once and feel the flow. It can be anything you like, as long as it suits your abilities and is something you enjoy.

- **Take up an instrument** – it's never too late to play the piano, the guitar, or whatever takes your fancy, whether or not you learnt as a child.

- **Join a choir** – feel your spirit soar with the rousing power of harmony.

- **Run** – thanks to initiatives like Parkrun and Couch to 5k, anyone can be a runner. So pull on some trainers and join the (running) crowd.

- **Play chess** – no one to play with? Download an app for a cerebral challenge.

- **Take up gardening** – don't wait until you retire to feel the benefits of being immersed in nature; get in the zone now.

- **Unleash your creativity** – adult coloring books not your thing? Try taking on a project such as upcycling a piece of old furniture, or even making something from scratch.

'Follow your passion. It will lead you to your purpose.'

Oprah Winfrey

FINAL LITTLE ACTS OF SELF-CARE

For the Mind

- **Use essential oils** – a few drops in a diffuser or bath is a gorgeous act of self-care. Try frankincense, lavender, ylang ylang, sandalwood or bergamot to promote relaxation and relieve stress. For a special treat, book an aromatherapy massage.

- **Get some creature comfort** – animals are great therapy. If you don't have a pet of your own, ask to borrow a friend's, become a dog walker, or visit a rescue center. You could even become a volunteer.

- **Have a clear-out** – it's not just about physical space, the junk we accumulate encroaches upon our mental space, too. Clutter can make us feel overwhelmed – plus it makes things harder to find! So recycle old paperwork, donate clothes you don't wear, and free your mind and your wardrobe.

- **Re-balance** – if you are employed and feel suffocated, talk to your boss about flexible or remote working. Could you even consider going freelance?

- **Make a list** – when you've got a million thoughts whizzing around your brain, writing them down can help you feel more calm and organized, and help you get to the right place at the right time.

- **Have a duvet day** – because sometimes all we want to do is burrow under the covers. So give yourself permission to hibernate, just for a day.

LITTLE ACTS OF
SELF-CARE FOR

The
Spirit

The spirit is that profound, elusive element of being that defies definition, yet has the capacity for incredible strength, growth and resourcefulness.

'Man never made any material as resilient as the human spirit.'

Bernard Williams

Whether or not you worship a god, practice organized religion or consider yourself to be spiritual, we all have a spirit. It's the place where we hold our core values and beliefs, where we feel hope and happiness, and where love begins.

In today's 24/7 world, little acts of self-care are vital for keeping the spirit singing and dancing. Without self-care, the spirit becomes weak and hoarse and we become like cogs caught in the machine of society. So however you define it – your soul, your essence, your deepest self – make time for your spirit and keep it a-l-i-v-e.

Essential

ACTS OF SELF-CARE FOR THE SPIRIT

- **Acknowledge your values** – try making a list of your top 10 and why they're important to you.

- **Invest in experiences rather than products** – research shows that spending money on experiences like camping, horse-riding and going to concerts brings greater happiness than spending money on things like shoes, clothes, cars and gadgets.

- **Make time for stillness** – this is often completely lacking in our 24/7 world. When was the last time you experienced pure tranquility?

- **Spend more time outdoors** – it's hard to over-estimate the benefits of spending time in nature for raising the spirits and diminishing stress.

- **Hang out with positive people** – because happiness and positivity are contagious.

- **Practise mindfulness** – be present in the here and now, rather than worrying about yesterday and tomorrow.

'We are all different. There is no such thing as a standard or run-of-the-mill human being, but we share the same human spirit.'

Stephen Hawking

QUICK FIX ACTS OF SELF-CARE FOR

The Spirit

When we're constantly wired, it's only a matter of time before we blow a fuse. See how many of these you can manage to keep your spirit in check.

- **Visit a flower market** – and revel in nature's prozac.

- **Hug a tree** – or try forest bathing, a Japanese therapy that involves absorbing the forest through our senses. It's based on evidence that being around trees and breathing in their essential oils, called phytoncides, helps to reduce stress and promote relaxation. It doesn't have to be a full-blown forest, just a place where there are trees.

- **Play** – as adults it's so easy to forget the simple delight of playing. So be silly, do a handstand, a cartwheel, a forward roll, splash in puddles, play Twister or charades, borrow a toddler (with permission!) and hug your inner child.

- **Watch the stars** – and marvel at the unfathomable wonders of the universe.

- **Spread good news** – and spread the love. Check out uplifting news sites like positive.news.

'When I'm not feeling my best I ask myself, "What are you gonna do about it?"I use the negativity to fuel the transformation into a better me.'

Beyonce

Practice Gratitude

Being grateful for the good things in our lives isn't just good manners, it's good science! In one famous study, the psychologist Martin Seligman found that people who spent ten minutes before bed writing down three things that went well that day experienced greater life satisfaction and less depression than those who didn't.

Why not try it for yourself? Buy a nice journal or diary and keep it next to your pillow. Each night, write down three things you're thankful for. They don't have to be a big deal – it could be as simple as the sun shining, eating your favorite sandwich for lunch, or someone making you a coffee or giving you a compliment.

'Appreciation is a wonderful thing: it makes what is excellent in others belong to us as well.'

Voltaire

'How
we need
another
soul to
cling to.'

Sylvia Plath

SAVOR THE MOMENT

Savoring is the practice of paying attention to the tiny things that make us happy every day. Unlike mindfulness which involves simply being in the moment, savoring requires actively tuning in to that moment.

Often, it's the things that make us stressed, scared or upset that grab our attention, but by resetting our minds to notice the positive things instead, we can boost our happiness levels and emotional resilience.

Learning to savor involves slowing down and prolonging everyday experiences. So, whether you're eating a delicious piece of fruit, or walking in nature, give it your full attention, using as many of your senses as possible to reflect on why it makes you feel so good.

The other benefit of savoring is that it switches our mindset from associating happiness with the big stuff such as a pay rise, a holiday or a new outfit, to enabling us to appreciate the little things.

GET CONNECTED

Just as our bodies need food and water to survive, the human spirit needs human connection.

Yet thanks to the changing structure of society and advances in technology, more of us feel alone than ever before. And it's not just the elderly; recent research reveals loneliness is a growing epidemic among younger people, too. Life changes such as leaving home, going to university, moving area, having a baby, starting a new job or being made redundant, can result in horrible isolation.

Loneliness doesn't just make you feel awful, it can have a negative impact on your physical health, too. Experts say the risks of feeling alone can be as significant as the risks of smoking and obesity.

So, dig deep and seek connection; it could be the most important act of self-care you try today.

'These days, loneliness is the new cancer – a shameful, embarrassing thing, brought upon yourself in some obscure way.'

Gail Honeyman,
Eleanor Oliphant is Completely Fine

LITTLE ACTS OF SELF-CARE FOR

Banishing Loneliness

Building connections with others may not be as difficult as you think. Try at least one of these this week.

- **Don't be a stranger** – however busy you are, make time for people: go the extra mile, rekindle old friendships, make the effort to keep in touch with people whose company you enjoy.

- **Volunteer** – it can be hard to get to know new people, especially if you're prone to shyness. But getting involved with an organization or charity gives you an excuse to meet new faces. Plus you'll be doing something useful.

- **Join in** – whether it's a team sport, an evening class, or a creative writing group, you'll get to meet new people at the same time as doing something you enjoy. All it takes is one email or phone call to get started.

- **Make the first move** – look out for the people who hang back from the crowd, the mom who stands alone at the school gate, the colleague who avoids communal areas, the neighbor who rarely leaves the house. So be the one to say 'hello' – you never know where it will take you.

- **Check out meetup.com** – it's full of local groups in thousands of cities for bringing people together to do all sorts of things from film nights to photography, board games to meditation.

TINY ACTS OF

Kindness

Try these tiny acts of kindness and see how good it feels to make someone else feel good.

- Hold the door open for someone.

- Give up your seat on a bus or train for somebody who looks weary.

- Allow someone who seems in a rush to jump ahead of you in a line.

- Let another driver out of traffic.

- Offer to help someone who's struggling to carry heavy luggage up steps.

- Say thank you to people who help you, regardless of whether or not it's their job.

- Park considerately – don't take up two spaces when one will do and only use priority spaces if you really need to.

- Make someone a cup of tea or coffee without being asked.

- Make (or buy) a batch of cookies to take to work, or share with friends.

'There is no exercise better for the heart than reaching down and lifting people up.'

John Holmes

Lend a Hand

Helping others is a great way to do good and practice self-care at the same time. That's because when we are kind to others, it causes our brains to release more of the 'feel good' chemicals that are linked to happiness and self-esteem. This creates a 'positive feedback loop' which encourages us to carry on being kind, raising our spirits even higher. Double whammy!

'May I never get too busy in my own affairs that I fail to respond to the needs of others with kindness and compassion.'

Thomas Jefferson

SELF-CARE
FOR THE SPIRIT

- **Do one thing on your to-do list** – if you've got a to-do list that's longer than your arm, do yourself a favor and complete one task that you've been putting off for ages. Better still, cancel a few chores from the list.

- **Read more** – books are good for you! Research suggests that reading not only keeps us engaged, but benefits our mental health and well-being too, and can even reduce the risk of dementia.

- **Print off a photograph from when you were young** – pin it up to remind you of good times, and as a prompt to stay in touch with your inner child.

- **Laugh** – laughter really is the best therapy and when you feel happy you're more likely to make other people feel happy, too.

- **String up some fairy lights** – well, why not?

AND LASTLY...

If you've finished reading this book, don't consign acts of self-care to the shelf, but carry on nourishing your body, mind and spirit for all that you're worth. Because self-care really is for life. And you're worth it.

'Yesterday I was clever, so I wanted to change the world. Today I am wise, so I am changing myself.'

Rumi